Elmo's
Christmas

Picture Puzzles & Songs

D1551142

Illustrated by Sue DiCicco, Warner McGee, and Sesame Workshop

"Sesame Workshop"®, "Sesame Street"®, and associated characters, trademarks, and design elements are owned
and licensed by Sesame Workshop. ©2011 Sesame Workshop. All Rights Reserved.

This publication may not be reproduced in whole or in part by any means whatsoever without written permission from the copyright owners.
Permission is never granted for commercial purposes.

Published by Louis Weber, C.E.O., Publications International, Ltd.

7373 North Cicero Avenue
Lincolnwood, Illinois 60712

Ground Floor, 59 Gloucester Place
London W1U 8JJ

Customer Service: 1-800-595-8484 or customer_service@pilbooks.com

www.pilbooks.com

p i kids is a trademark of Publications International, Ltd., and is registered in the United States.

Look and Find is a tradmark of Publications International, Ltd., and is registered in the United States and Canada.

publications international, ltd.

Spot these things in the snow.

Jingle Bells

Jingle bells, jingle bells,
Jingle all the way!
Oh, what fun it is to ride
In a one-horse open sleigh. Hey!

Now search for five differences
between the two pictures.
For the solution, turn to page 14.

Jingle bells, jingle bells,
Jingle all the way!
Oh, what fun it is to ride
In a one-horse open sleigh. Hey!

Search for these wintry items near the ice.

Here We Come A-Caroling

Here we come a-caroling
Among the leaves so green.
Here we come a-wandering
So fair to be seen.

Now find five things that are different
in the two ice-skating pictures.
For the solution, turn to page 14.

 Love and joy come to you,
And to you glad tidings, too.
And God bless you and send you
A happy New Year,
And God send you a happy New Year.

Find these holiday things around the tree.

O Christmas Tree

O Christmas tree, O Christmas tree,
How lovely are your branches!
O Christmas tree, O Christmas tree,
How lovely are your branches!

Now look for five things that are
different in the two pictures.
For the solution, turn to page 15.

Your boughs are green in summer's glow,
And do not fade in winter's snow.
O Christmas tree, O Christmas tree,
How lovely are your branches!

Deck the Halls

♪ Deck the halls with boughs of holly,
Fa-la-la-la-la, la-la-la-la.
'Tis the season to be jolly,
Fa-la-la-la-la, la-la-la-la. ♪

Now search for five differences
in the two pictures.
For the solution, turn to page 15.

  Don we now our gay apparel,
Fa-la-la, la-la-la, la-la-la.
Troll the ancient yuletide carol,
Fa-la-la-la-la, la-la-la-la.

Up on the Housetop

Up on the housetop reindeer pause,
Out jumps good old Santa Claus!
Down through the chimney with lots of toys,
All for the little ones' Christmas joys.

Now find five differences between
the two pictures.
For the solution, turn to page 16.

Ho ho ho! Who wouldn't go?
   Ho ho ho! Who wouldn't go?
Up on the housetop, click, click, click!
   Down through the chimney with good St. Nick.

Find these things at the holiday celebration.

We Wish You a Merry Christmas

We wish you a merry Christmas,
We wish you a merry Christmas,
We wish you a merry Christmas,
And a happy New Year!

Now look for five things that are different
in the two party pictures.
For the solution, turn to page 16.

Good tidings we bring
To you and your kin,
Good tidings for Christmas,
And a happy New Year!

This is the answer
key to the
Picture Puzzle on
pages 2 & 3.

This is the answer
key to the
Picture Puzzle on
pages 4 & 5.

SAFE TO
SKATE

This is the answer key to the Picture Puzzle on pages 6 & 7.

This is the answer key to the Picture Puzzle on pages 8 & 9.

This is the answer key to the Picture Puzzle on pages 10 & 11.

This is the answer key to the Picture Puzzle on pages 12 & 13.